Whose Hat Is That?

by RON ROY

photographs by
ROSMARIE HAUSHERR

Clarion Books

TICKNOR & FIELDS: A HOUGHTON MIFFLIN COMPANY

New York

For Mary Gambill, a good friend to animals, children, and writers.

R.R.

Photographer's Note:
My thanks to all the parents, children, teachers, and friends who have participated in photo-sessions, helped with valuable information, or lent me their hats and props for this book. Special thanks to: New England Culinary Institute, Montpelier, Vermont; Metro Bicycle Stores, New York City; George Gilbert, magician, New York City; Amtrak; Barnet & Peacham Volunteer Fire Department, Vermont; Dutch Girl Painters, New York City; New York Racing Association, Inc.; Allan Greenleaf, Peacham, Vermont; Lyndon Institute football team, Vermont; New York City Park & Recreation Department; New York City Department of Transportation, Bureau of Highways; the Marunas family; Dr. Kim Kahng; Cody McCone; the Fraiman family; the Hildreth family; Corlears School, New York City; Nazareth Nursery School, New York City.

Clarion Books
Ticknor & Fields, a Houghton Mifflin Company
Text copyright © 1987 by Ron Roy
Photographs copyright © 1987 by Rosmarie Hausherr

Library of Congress Cataloging-in-Publication Data
Roy, Ron, 1940-
   Whose hat is that?
   Summary: Text and photographs portray the appearance
and function of eighteen types of hats, including a
top hat, jockey's cap, and football helmet.
   1. Hats—Juvenile literature.   [1. Hats]   I. Hausherr,
Rosmarie, ill.   II. Title.
GT2110.R69   1987   391′.43   86-17553
ISBN 0-89919-446-X

H   10 9 8 7 6 5 4 3 2 1

Do you have a favorite hat? Why do you wear it? Many people wear hats to protect their heads. Others wear hats to pretend they are someone else. Some people wear hats just for fun!

You will see many different hats in this book. Maybe you will even see your own favorite hat! Before you begin to read, why not put on your special hat?

Who wears a straw hat
with a wide brim?

People who sit or play in the hot sun often wear a hat woven of straw. The wide brim of the hat shades the face and protects it from sunburn. Straw hats are lightweight and cool. Do you wear a straw hat in the summertime?

Why does this hat
cover the face?

People who play or work outside in cold weather must dress warmly. This wool hat keeps the head, nose, ears, chin, and cheeks warm. You can breathe right through the wool. Wearing this hat, you can fool your friends. They won't know who you are!

Who wears a waterproof hat that dips down in the back?

Many people wear these hats when it rains. Workers who build and repair streets and highways often wear these waterproof hats, too. The hats are bright yellow, so people driving in traffic will see the workers. Rainwater drips off the sloping rim in the back instead of sliding down the person's neck. On windy days, these hats can be tied under the chin. Who wants to chase a hat on a windy, rainy day?

Why does this hat have a net
that covers the face and neck?

This is a beekeeper's hat. When beekeepers collect honey from their beehives, they may get stung. To protect themselves from bee stings, beekeepers hang nets made of fine mesh from their special hats. The bees cannot fly through the tiny holes in the mesh. A tight string at the bottom stops the bees from flying under the net.

Who wears a hat shaped
like a turtle's shell?

Builders must wear these hard hats when they work on construction sites. Builders work with heavy materials. They move lumber and steel, pour concrete, and lay bricks. The hard hat will protect the worker if something heavy falls on him or her. Hard hats also protect the workers if they accidentally bump their heads.

Why is this hat covered
with colored splotches?

Have you ever gotten paint in your hair? If you have, you know why painters wear these hats. Painting is messy work! These caps cover the hair and shield the face from paint splatters. Sometimes painters are given these hats for free when they buy paint. They throw the hats away when the paint job is finished.

Who wears this tall, white hat?

Only the chef, who is in charge of the kitchen, wears the tall, white hat. The cooks wear floppy hats. Together, they prepare food in a restaurant. The heat from the stoves makes the kitchen hot. If the chef and cooks perspire, the hatbands keep the sweat from dripping into their eyes. The hats also stop hair from falling into the food.

Who wears a stretchy rubber cap
to cover the hair?

Many people wear thin rubber caps when they swim. The caps protect the hair from salt in the ocean and chlorine in swimming pools. The hats also keep the swimmers' hair out of their eyes. Swimmers who race can swim faster with their hair covered. They slip through the water like seals!

Who wears a snug helmet
that buckles under the chin?

Jockeys wear these helmets for protection when they ride in horse races. If a jockey is thrown from a horse, the hard helmet will protect his or her head. The straps and buckle keep the helmet in place. Look closely and you will see that the helmet is covered with a silk cap. This is so the helmet will match the jockey's colorful riding outfit.

Who wears a paper cap that
completely covers the hair?

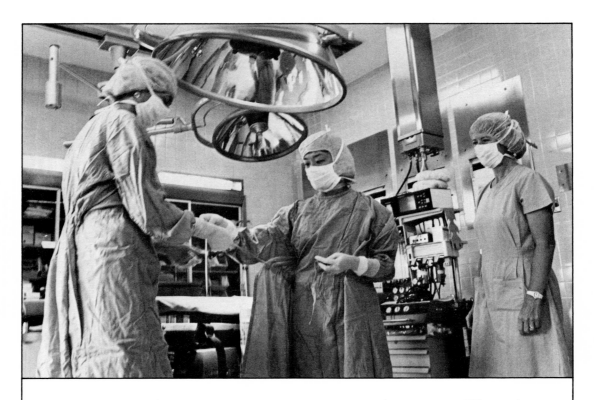

Surgeons and operating-room nurses wear these caps. They also wear face masks, gowns, and rubber gloves. People who work in operating rooms wear this clothing so that germs from their hair, sweat, or breath do not get on the patients. The caps, as well as the masks and gloves, are thrown away after the operation. The gowns are washed and sterilized to make them free from germs. Then the gowns can be used again.

Who wears a helmet
with sloping edges?

Fighting a fire can be very dangerous work. Firefighters wear hard helmets to protect their heads and necks from sparks, falling objects, and water. They also wear fire-resistant suits. Some firefighters lower face shields on their helmets to keep sparks out of their eyes. One firefighter in the picture wears a special mask. It is connected to an oxygen tank worn on his back. If he goes into a burning building, he can still breathe, even in the heavy smoke caused by the fire.

Who would wear this elegant,
tall hat?

Long ago, men wore these hats on special occasions, such as fancy parties, weddings, or important meetings. They are called top hats. Now many people wear these elegant hats. For example, some dancers wear top hats when they perform. Magicians sometimes use top hats when they do tricks. What a good place to hide flowers, cards, or scarves!

Which is the most popular cap
of all?

It is the baseball player's cap. Players wear these caps to keep their hair out of their eyes. The stiff visor on the front of the cap shades the eyes from the sun. The caps are soft so players can stuff them into a pocket. Most baseball caps have the team's name or initials on the front. Do you wear a baseball cap?

Why does this helmet have bars
in front of the face?

This is a football helmet. Football is an exciting sport, but it can also be dangerous. Players get knocked to the ground and often bang their heads. These strong helmets prevent injury to the player's head and neck. The bars in the face guard protect the nose, mouth, and jaw. The helmets are padded on the inside and fastened securely with the chin guard. Can you guess why these helmets have holes over the ears?

Why does this cap have a
special badge over the visor?

This cap is part of a uniform. The badge says Conductor. When train travelers need a conductor's help, they look for a man or woman wearing this special cap. Uniform caps are also worn by pilots, police officers, bus drivers, mail deliverers, or others whose job is helping people. The uniform cap is like a sign that asks, "May I help you?"

Who wears a western hat
with a wide, curved brim?

Brenda Allen

Men and women who work around horses and cattle on ranches wear these hats. Ranches and rodeos are dusty places. The wide brims keep dust off the workers' heads and sun out of their eyes. The curved brims catch rainwater so it doesn't run down their backs. A sweatband inside the hat absorbs perspiration before it drips into their eyes. How many western hats can you see in this picture?

When do you wear a hat
decorated with flowers and lace?

You may want to wear a special hat when you celebrate a special event. Some people wear dressy hats to parties. Many people wear them to church or synagogue. Others like to dress up to celebrate the coming of spring! Some people decorate their own hats. They use ribbons, lace, flowers, or even berries. How would you decorate a special hat?

Who wears a flat cap with a tassel hanging on the side?

When students graduate from school, they often wear these caps with gowns at their graduation ceremony. Before the ceremony, the cap's tassel hangs on the right side of the student's face. At the same moment near the end of the ceremony, each student moves the tassel to the left side. This means the students have graduated. They toss their caps into the air. Hurray!